Core Knowledge Language Arts®

Unit 1
Workbook

Skills Strand
GRADE 1

Amplify learning.

Core Knowledge®

ISBN 978-1-61700-200-7

Printed in the USA
08 LSCOW 2021

Unit 1
Workbook

This Workbook contains worksheets that accompany many of the lessons from the *Teacher Guide* for Unit 1. Each worksheet is identified by the lesson number in which it is used. The worksheets in this book do not include written instructions for students because the instructions would have words that are not decodable. Teachers will explain these worksheets to the students orally, using the instructions in the Teacher Guide. The Workbook is a student component, which means each student should have a Workbook.

Name _____

Dear Family Member,

It is exciting to start the school year–a warm welcome back to you and your child!

During the early weeks of school, we will review the skills taught in Kindergarten. This review period will also give us the opportunity to get to know your child better so we can identify his or her particular areas of strength and weakness in reading. It is important that we determine exactly what level of instruction is most appropriate for your child.

Once we have completed our evaluations, your child will be placed in the instructional materials most appropriate for his or her learning needs. You will begin to see more examples of class work, as well as homework, on a regular basis.

It is important that parents become involved in the education of their child. If you would like information on how you can help your child at home, please do not hesitate to contact me. You will continue to receive periodic parent letters that will give you tips and activities to do with your child at home. I look forward to teaching your child this year and helping each student to grow as a reader!

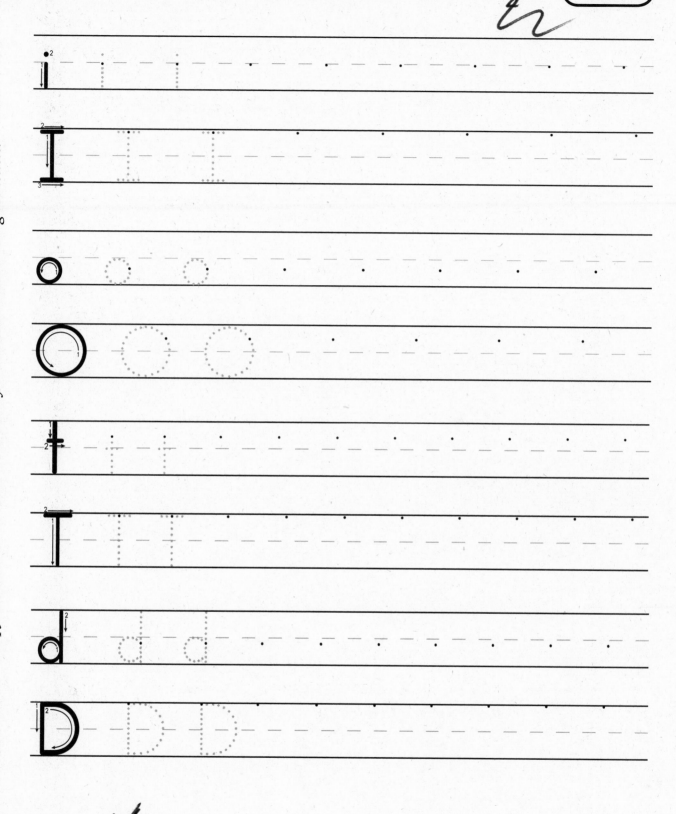

Directions: Have the student trace and copy the letters. The student should say the sounds while writing the letters.

| cat | pot | dot |
| dad | cap | dig |

_____

- - - - - - - - - - - - -

_____

Directions: Have the student write each word under its matching picture.

_____

- - - - - - - - - - - - -

_____

Dear Family Member:

Ask your child to cut out the letter cards. Arrange the cards to make the word cat. Have your child read the word, sound by sound. Repeat with the following words: *pat, pot, pit, nap, it, got, dog, dig, not.* If your child does well reading the words, read the words aloud one at a time, and ask him to spell the word by arranging the letter cards.

a	p	n
c	g	i
o	t	d

pan   dot   dad

dog   pin   nap

| a dog | mom and dad |
| a fat pig | a tin can |

Directions: Have the student write each phrase under its matching picture.

_____

_____

_____

_____

_____

TAKE HOME

Dear Family Member,

   Your child has been taught to read words by saying the sounds and then blending them together to make a word. Below are some words your child should be able to read with practice. Ask your child to cut out the word cards. Show the cards to your child and have him or her read them. Please encourage your child to read the words by saying individual sounds and then blending them together to make a word. The words marked with a star are Tricky Words. These are words that are not pronounced as students may expect; we say that Tricky Words do not play by the rules. As an extension of this activity, ask your child to copy the words onto a sheet of paper. Please keep the word cards for future practice.

fat	did	pig
and	dog	not
mad	cat	mats
vet	damp	gift
★ a	★ I	

1.	met	man	mat	bat
2.	zip	zap	sip	vat
3.	cut	cot	got	gut
4.	pet	vet	vat	fat
5.	rot	rob	rod	red
6.	fox	fix	fax	fan
7.	spill	grab	stop	spit
8.	clip	drip	drop	drum
9.	cabs	dogs	crabs	crust
10.	flint	flag	print	flap
11.	mess	mass	miss	muss

12.	kong	king	kin	ken
13.	wack	wax	wick	wicks
14.	ships	chops	chips	chaps
15.	chin	shin	shun	sin
16.	that	fin	this	thin
17.	chin	jill	chill	spill
18.	quest	chest	quill	best
19.	bus	buzz	boss	buff
20.	ebb	edd	odd	bibb

21.	the	was	of	to
22.	a	from	your	are
23.	have	one	who	their
24.	you	said	were	says
25.	here	I	is	no

Scoring Sheet for Word Recognition Test

Lines	Code Knowledge Tested	Items Correct	Specific Errors
1–6	CVC word with single-letter spellings, e.g., *fax*, *fat*	___/6	Sound spellings missed and/or confusion, e.g., 'b' and 'd', 's' and 'z', 'a', and 'o'
7–13	Consonant clusters, e.g., 'dr' in *drip*	___/7	Clusters missed:
14–20	Consonant digraphs and double-letter spellings, e.g., 'ss' and 'th'	___/7	Consonant digraphs/double-letter spellings missed:
21–25	Tricky Words, e.g., *the* and *I*	___/5	Tricky Words missed:

Total Score: _____ /20

- Students who scored **18 out of 20 (90%)** or above have strong word recognition skills and are making good progress. They will next take the **Story Reading Test, "Gwen's Hens."**
- Students who scored **17 or less** should be assessed one-on-one. They will first receive the **Pseudoword Reading Test.**

Seth

This is **Se**th Smi**th**.

Seth is ten.

Seth must get in bed at ten.

Seth can jump on his bed, but not past ten.

Seth can stomp and romp and stand on his hands, but not past ten.

Seth's dad gets mad if **Se**th is not in bed at ten.

Seth's Mom

This is Pat.

Pat is Se**th**'s mom.

Pat can fix **thing**s.

Pat can scrub, plan, and think.

Pat is stro**ng.**

Pat can run fast.

Pat can si**ng** so**ng**s.

Kit

Kit can run.

Kit can skip.

Kit can flip and flop.

Kit can swim.

Kit and Stan

Kit ran and hid.

Stan ran and got Kit.

Stan ran and hid.

Kit ran and got Stan.

Kit and Stan had fun.

Gwen's Hens

Gwen had a red hen.

Gwen kept the hen in a pen.

The hen sat on its eggs.

It sat and sat and sat.

When Gwen got up, the hen was still on
its eggs.

When Gwen went to bed, the hen was
still there.

Then the hen was a mom!

1. Gwen had a:

    ○ dog

    ○ cat

    ○ hen

2. The hen was:

    ○ wet

    ○ red

    ○ mad

3. Gwen kept the hen in a:

    ○ box

    ○ pen

    ○ pet

4. The hen sat on:

      ○ a bed

      ○ a mat

      ○ its eggs

5. When Gwen went went to bed, the hen:

      ○ sat and sat

      ○ had a snack

      ○ went with Gwen

6. The hen sat and sat and was a:

      ○ kid

      ○ dad

      ○ mom

Pseudoword Scoring Sheet

Directions: If a student misreads a word, write the letter for the sound that is misread above the corresponding letter in the word. If student reads "wug" as /wag/, mark "wug" as follows: a̸/wug

CVC Words	1. wug rab sep zat het
CVC Words	2. kem jid pog lum yod
CVC Words	3. lin fod cax ved mip
Consonant Cluster	4. nist brin clup stent glosp
Consonant Digraphs	5. thock shup chim quib ling
Double-Letter Spellings	6. muzz vell tass beff dagg

Words correct _____ / 30

Error Analysis

Short Vowel Letter-Sound Errors:

Consonant Letter-Sound Errors:

Consonant Cluster Errors:

Consonant Digraph Errors:

Double-Letter Spellings

Code Knowledge Diagnostic Test

1.	m	s	f	v	z
2.	r	l	n	e	u
3.	I	o	a	t	y
4.	d	g	h	j	k
5.	b	p	c	w	x
6.	sh	ch	th	ng	qu
7.	ff	ss	ll	gg	ck

Letter/sounds correct _____ / 35

Letter Name Test

1.	a	w	e
2.	t	y	u
3.	o	p	s
4.	f	g	h
5.	k	l	z
6.	c	v	b
7.	d	x	j
8.	n	i	m
9.	u	r	q
10.	l	y	g

Letter names correct _____ / 10

Seth's Dad

This is Ted.

Ted is Se**th**'s dad.

Ted is stro**ng**.

Ted can **ch**op big logs wi**th** his ax.

Ted can lift big
stumps.

Ted can cru**sh** tin
cans wi**th** his hands.

Sal's Fish Shop

Pat and Se**th** went in Sal's
Fi**sh Sh**op.

Sal had fresh fish.

Sal had fresh shrimp.

Sal had crabs.

Sal had clams.

Sal had squid.

Pat got fish and shrimp.

1. flip flops

2. big drop

3. tin can

4. red mat

5. big hat

6. mom and dad

Kit's Hats

Kit ha**s** hats.

Kit ha**s** big hats.

Kit has flat hats.

Kit has fun hats.

Kit's cats lap up milk.

Kit's cats jump up on Kit's bed.

Kit's Cats

Kit has cats.

Kit's cats run fast.

Lunch

Se**th** had lun**ch** wi**th** his mom and dad.

Pat had **sh**rimp and **ch**ips.

Ted had **sh**rimp, fi**sh**, and **ch**ips.

Se**th** had ham and **ch**ips.

Mun**ch**, mun**ch**.

Crun**ch**, crun**ch**.

Yum, yum.

Seth's Finch

That's S**eth**'s pet fin**ch**, **Ch**ip.

Chip can flap his wi**ng**s.

Chip can mun**ch** on ants and bugs.

Chip can si**ng**.

Chip can land on S**eth**'s hand.

That fin**ch** is fun!

Directions: Have students draw a picture for each phrase.

1. big dog

2. red cap

3. mad Dad

4. fat cat

5. wet frog

6. pig and hen

Kit's Mom

Kit's mom gets up at six.

Kit's mom gets dad up.

Kit's mom gets Kit up.

Kit's mom gets dad fed.

Kit's mom gets Kit fed.

Kit's mom gets Kit's pets fed

Mumps

Kit ha**s** mumps.

Kit i**s** in bed.

Kit can't get up.

Kit can't run and jump.

Kit can't skip and hop.

Kit i**s** sad.

Lost Finch

Seth's pet finch, Chip, is lost.

Seth can't spot him.

Pat can't spot him.

Ted can't spot him.

Chip is not on Seth's bed.

Chip is not on Seth's desk.

Then, at last, Pat spots Chip.

Chip hid in Pat's hat and slept.

Seth's Sled

Seth's sled went fast.

Seth held on.

Seth hit bumps but did not stop.

Seth hit slush but did not stop.

Then Seth's sled hit mud.

Splash!

Seth got mud on his sled.

Seth got mud on his pants.

Seth got mud on his hat.

Directions: Have students draw a picture for each phrase.

1. a cup

2. wet mop

3. big log

4. red ball

5. sad pal

6. hot dog

Up

Kit gets up on top.

Kit helps Max get up.

Max helps Jen get up.

Jen helps Kent get up.

Kent helps Ted get up.

Ted helps Peg get up.

Fast Fred

Kit's pal Fred gulps his milk.

Fast Fred gulps and gulps.

Fred gets milk on his desk.

Fred gets milk on his pants.

Fred gets milk on Kit.

Kit gets mad at Fred.

"Stop it, Fred!"

Meg's Tots

This is Meg.
Meg is Pat's best pal.

Pat has 1 lad—Se**th**.
Meg has 5 tots—Tom, Tim,
Max, Sam, and Wes.
Meg has **qu**ints!

Pat and Ted help Meg.
Pat sets Tim and Tom on
Se**th**'s rug.
Ted sets Sam on Se**th**'s **qu**ilt.
Pat sets Max on Se**th**'s bed.
Ted helps Wes stand up on
Se**th**'s desk.

Hash and Milk

Pat and Ted had lun**ch** wi**th**
Meg's tots.

Max got ha**sh** on his **ch**in.

Wes got ha**sh** on his bib.

Tim's milk is on Tom.

Then Tom got milk on Tim.

Sam got milk on Pat and
Ted.

Pip's Cats

Pip i**s** Kit's pal.

Pip ha**s** six cats.

Pip's cats got in mud.

Pip's cats left mud on hi**s** rug.

Pip's mom got mad.

Vic Gets Lost

Pip's cat Vic got lost.

Pip felt sad.

Kit ran and got Vic.

Kit set Vic on Pip's lap.

Pip felt glad.

Directions: Tell students to cut out the letters and see how many words they can make. Ask them to write the words on a piece of paper.

b̲	x	l
u̲	o	j
g	r	n̲

fan	van	zip
sit	fin	cats

_____
- - - - - - - - - - - -
_____

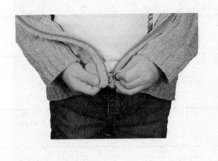

_____
- - - - - - - - - - - -
_____

Directions: Have the student trace and copy the letters. The student should say the sounds while writing the letters.

f

F

v

V

s

S

z

Z

Directions: Have the student cut out the letter cards.

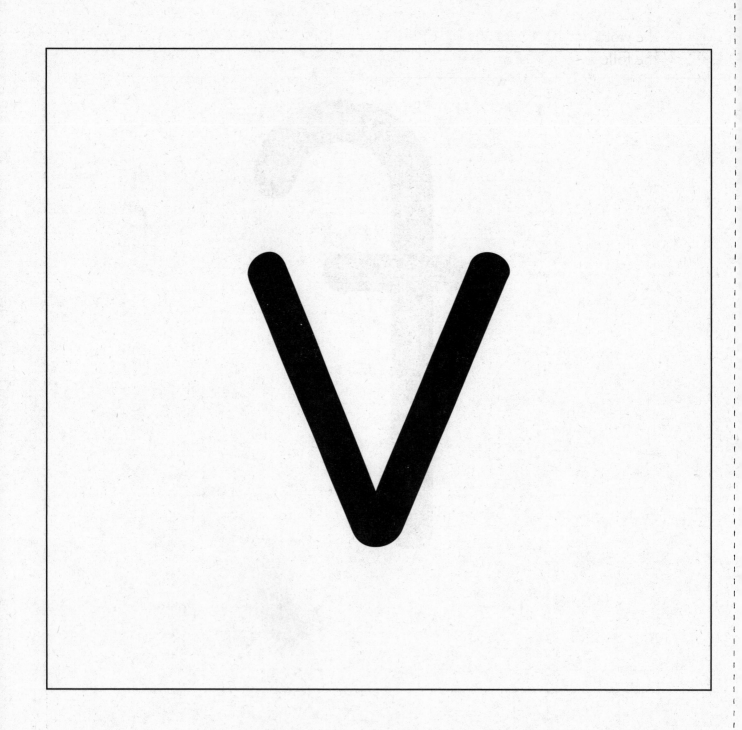

Dear Family Member,

Ask your child to cut out the letter cards and arrange the cards to make the word *sit.* Have your child read the word, sound by sound. Repeat with the following words: *sat, mat, man, van, hit, hat, fit, fan, in.* If your child does well reading the words, read the words aloud one at a time and ask your child to spell the word by arranging the letter cards.

s	m	f
n	i	t
a	h	v

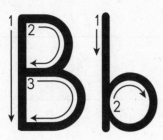 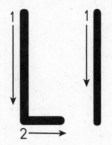 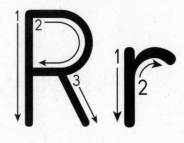

Directions: Have the student trace and copy the letters. The student should say the sounds while writing the letters.

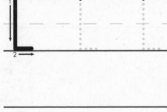

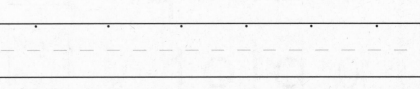

1. (r)(a)(t)

2. land

3. trip

4. lip

5. trim

6. stop

7. hip

8. cup

9. drop

10. plot

3	r a t

1. bed

2. lamp

3. nest

4. rug

Directions: Have the student write each word under its matching picture.

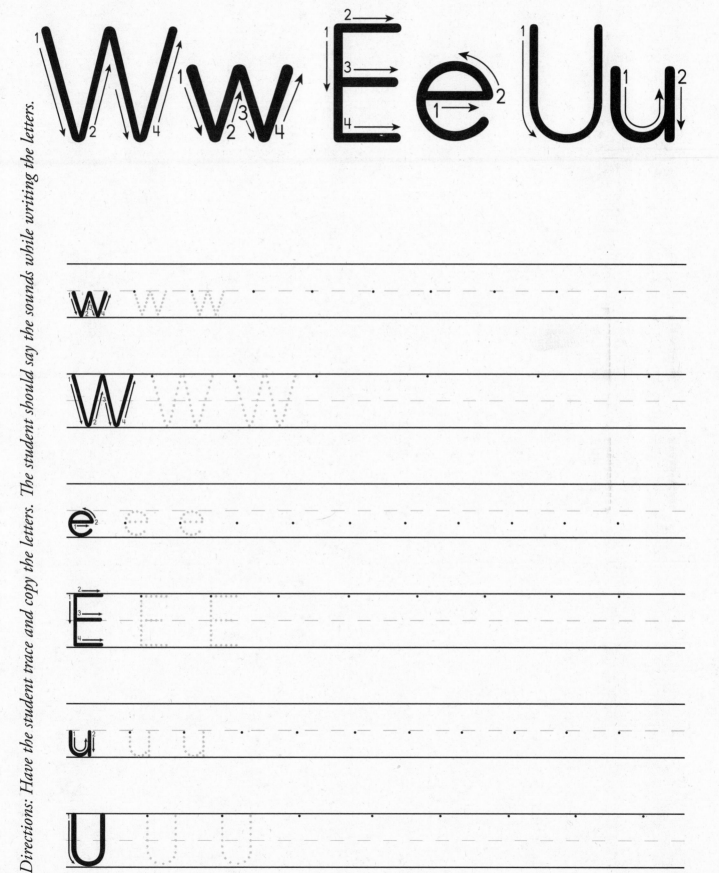

Directions: Have the student trace and copy the letters. The student should say the sounds while writing the letters.

Directions: Read the Tricky Words in the box. Say and then write the Tricky Words in each sentence in the space provided below.

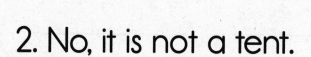

a   I   no   to   all   of   is

1. It is a big bus.

is   a

2. No, it is not a tent.

| a | I | no | to | all | of | is |

3. all of us

4. a hint of it

4. I went to bed.

TAKE HOME

Dear Family Member,

Ask your child to cut out the word cards and arrange the cards to make phrases. You may ask your child to copy the phrases onto a sheet of paper. Modifications: Arrange the cards yourself and have your child read the phrases. Note that the tricky parts in Tricky Words are underlined in gray. Please keep the cards for future practice. Remember that the words marked with a star are Tricky Words, which are words that don't play by the spelling rules.

★ all	rest	★ to
must	sit	run
in	cats	★ some
men	bed	wet
★ a	★ I	★ no

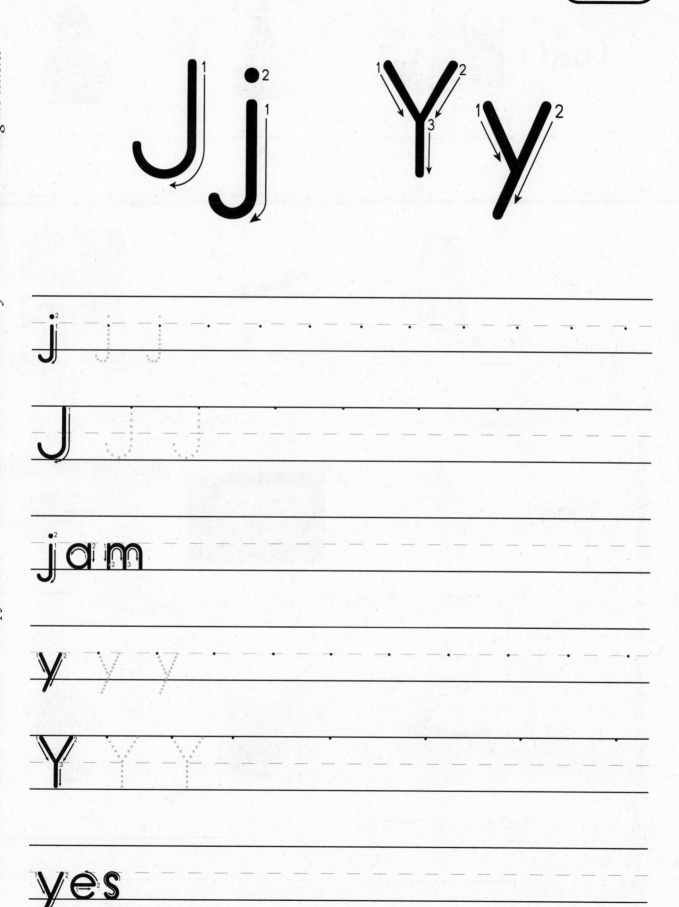

Directions: Have the student trace and copy the letters and words. The student should say the sounds while writing the letters.

j

J

jam

y

Y

yes

1. bed

2. jet

3. jog

4. jam

Dear Family Member,

Ask your child to cut out the word cards and arrange the cards to make phrases. You may ask your child to copy the phrases onto a sheet of paper. Modification: Arrange the cards yourself and have your child read the phrases. Note that the tricky parts in Tricky Words are underlined in gray. Please keep the cards for future practice.

and	*have	rug
fast	sad	mad
jumps	gets	red
dog	frog	bug
*are	*were	yes

Directions: Have the student trace and copy the letters and words. The student should say the sounds while writing the letters.

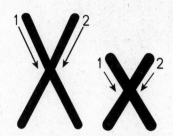
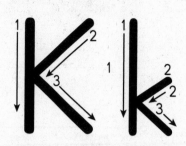

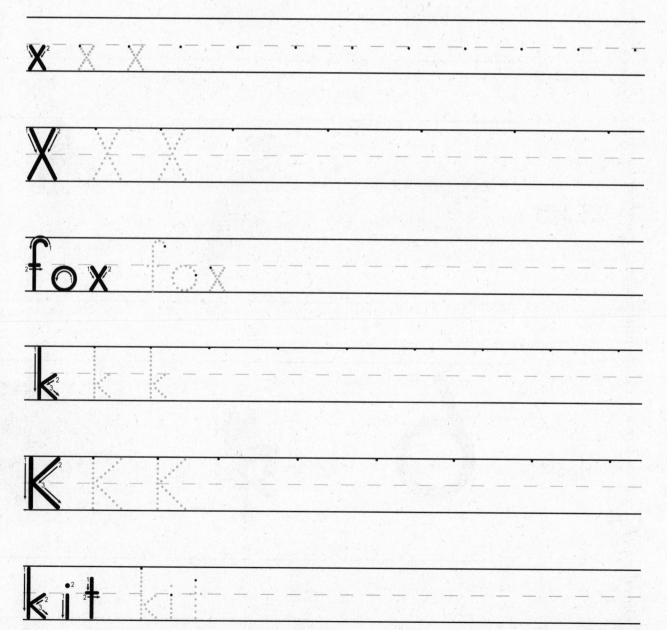

1. box

2. mix

3. kid

4. six

Name ______________________________

17.1

ch sh

ch

ch

chop

sh

sh

shop

Directions: Have the student trace and copy the letters and words. The student should say the sounds while writing the letters.

ship	chimp	chips
fish	bench	dish

_____

_____

_____

_____

_____

_____

Directions: Have the student write each word under its matching picture.

114 _Unit 1_

Dear Family Member,

Your child has been taught to read Tricky Words. Tricky Words are hard to read because they contain parts that are not pronounced the way one would expect. Have your child read the Tricky Words in the box and the sentences below. Note that the tricky parts of the Tricky Words are underlined in gray. Have your child write the matching Tricky Words for each sentence on the line. Extension: Have your child copy the completed sentences on a blank sheet of paper or dictate the sentences to your child.

is	two	to
are	from	do

1. Mom and dad _____ mad.

2. Max _____ six.

3. Dad had _____ cats.

4. Mom went _____ bed.

5. Just _____ it!

6. That gift is _____ dad.

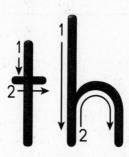

th

th

thin

bath

that

this

| bath | moth |
| cloth | fifth |

 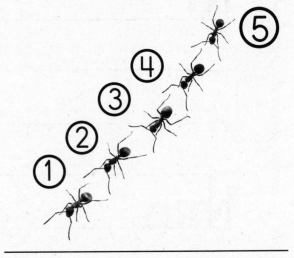

_____

- - - - - - - - - - - - - - -

_____

_____

- - - - - - - - - - - - - - -

_____

Directions: Have the student write each word under its matching picture.

TAKE HOME

Dear Family Member,

Your child has been taught to read words with the digraphs 'ch' as in *chips*, 'sh' as in *shin*, and 'th' as in *thin* or *then*. Below are some words your child should be able to read with practice. Ask your child to cut out the word cards. Show the cards to your child and have him or her read them. Please encourage your child to read the words by saying sounds and then blending them to make a word. As an extension of this activity, ask your child to copy the words onto a sheet of paper. Please keep the word cards for future practice.

dish	chop	shelf
that	brush	rich
this	chin	bath
shop	thin	much

Beth

1. Who went on top of a path at the pond?

_____
- - - - - - - - - - - - - - - - - -
_____
- - - - - - - - - - - - - - - - - -
_____
- - - - - - - - - - - - - - - - - -
_____

2. Who got some snap shots?

_____
- - - - - - - - - - - - - - - - - -
_____
- - - - - - - - - - - - - - - - - -
_____
- - - - - - - - - - - - - - - - - -
_____

3. Did Beth get a snap shot of a cat?

_____

- - - - - - - - - - - - - - -

_____

- - - - - - - - - - - - - - -

_____

- - - - - - - - - - - - - - -

_____

4. Dad got a snap shot of . . .

- ○ a fish.

- ○ Mom.

- ○ Beth.

ng qu

ng ng ng

ng

song

qu qu qu

qu

quit

Directions: Have the student trace and copy the letters and words. The student should say the sounds while writing the letters.

quilt	sing	king
swing	fang	strong

_____
- - - - - - - - - - - -
_____

_____
- - - - - - - - - - - -
_____

_____
- - - - - - - - - - - -
_____

_____
- - - - - - - - - - - -
_____

_____
- - - - - - - - - - - -
_____

_____
- - - - - - - - - - - -
_____

Directions: Have the student write each word under its matching picture.

124 Unit 1

Nat

1. Beth and Nat met . . .

   ○ in the U.K.

   ○ at camp.

   ○ on a bus.

2. Who got a lot of snap shots of Nat?

   _____
   -
   _____
   _____
   -
   _____
   _____

Directions: Have the student reread the story and answer the questions.

3. Beth got a snap shot of Nat with

○ a mask on.

○ a frog.

○ a fish.

4. Who got a job in the U.K.?

_____

- - - - - - - - - - - - - - - -

_____

- - - - - - - - - - - - - - - -

_____

- - - - - - - - - - - - - - - -

_____

- - - - - - - - - - - - - - - -

Dear Family Member,

Ask your child to cut out the letter cards. Have your child arrange the cards to make a series of real words and/or silly words (e.g. *shup*). Have your child read the words. Discuss whether each word is real or silly. Modification: Arrange the cards yourself and have your child read the words. Extension: Have your child copy the words onto a sheet of paper. Please keep the cards for future practice.

ch	p	i	s
m	a	j	z
u	sh	x	th
qu	b	t	o
w	e	ng	g

a e

o u

i

Directions: Have the student cut out the letter cards.

The Trip to the U.K.

Directions: Have the student reread the story and answer the questions.

1. Mom and Beth went to the U.K. on

   ○ a bus.

   ○ a ship.

   ○ a jet.

2. Who had a nap on the jet?

   _____

   _____

   _____

   _____

3. Who met Mom and Beth at the end of the ramp?

_____

- -

_____

- -

_____

- -

_____

- -

4. Beth slept...

○ next to Nat and Mom.

○ next to Dot.

○ on a rug.

Bud the Cat

The vet had to fix Bud's leg.

Nat's mom let him have Bud.

Bud had a bad leg.

Bud sat in a box with a cast on one leg.

Directions: Have the student paste the sentences from Worksheet 22.1 onto this worksheet in the correct order. Then have the student illustrate each sentence.

1.	2.
3.	4.

Dear Family Member,

This is a story your child has read at school. Encourage your child to read the story to you and talk about it together. Note that the tricky parts of the Tricky Words are underlined in gray.

Bud the Cat

This is a snap shot of Nat's cat, Bud.

Nat got Bud from a vet.

Bud had a bad leg.

The vet had to fix Bud's leg.

Bud had to sit in a box with a cast on one leg.

Then Nat said, "Mom, can I have him? Can I? Can I? Can I?"

Dot said yes.

The Fish

1. Nat got . . . .

    ○ fish.

    ○ t<u>wo</u> cats.

    ○ <u>one</u> dog.

2. The fish munch on . . .

    ○ a hot dog.

    ○ chips.

    ○ fish snacks.

Directions: Have the student reread the story and answer the questions.

3. Can the cat smell the fish?

_____
- -
_____
- -
_____
- -
_____
- -
_____

4. Can the cat get the fish?

_____
- -
_____
- -
_____
- -
_____
- -
_____

Dear Family Member,

This is a story your child has read at school. Encourage your child to read the story to you and talk about it together. Note that the tricky parts of the Tricky Words are underlined in gray.

The Fish

This is a snap shot of Nat's fish.

The fish swim and splash and munch on fish snacks.

The cat can smell the fish.

It can press on the glass.

It can grab at the fish.

But it can not get them.

Directions: Have the student read the words in the box and underline all of the spellings for /k/. Then have the student write the words that contain the /k/ sound spelled 'c' under the /k/ > 'c' header, the words that contain the /k/ sound spelled 'k' under the /k/ > 'k' header, and the words that contain the /k/ sound spelled 'ck' under the /k/ > 'ck' header.

cat	king	cost
kit	sock	pick
Jack	cot	camp

/k/ > 'c'

/k/ > 'k'

/k/ > 'ck'

Dear Family Member,

    Ask your child to cut out the word cards and arrange the cards to make phrases. Ask your child to copy the phrases onto a sheet of paper. Modification: Arrange the cards yourself and have your child read the phrases. Note that the tricky parts in Tricky Words are underlined in gray. Please keep the cards for future practice.

his	★ all	pigs
strong	★ two	with
★ have	run	★ the
kick	sniff	legs

The Flag Shop

1. The U.K. flag has . . .

   ○ a red dot.

   ○ a black box.

   ○ a red cross.

2. Who went to the shop?

   _____
   - - - - - - - - - - - - - - - - - -
   _____
   - - - - - - - - - - - - - - - - - -
   _____
   _____
   - - - - - - - - - - - - - - - - - -
   _____
   - - - - - - - - - - - - - - - - - -
   _____

Directions: Have the student reread the story and answer the questions.

Directions: In line 4, have the students mark the nouns that name a thing; in line 5, have them mark the nouns that name a person; in line 6, have them mark nouns.

3. <u>Who</u> is in the snap shot <u>of</u> the <u>U.K.</u> flag?

_____

- - - - - - - - - - - - - - - - - -

_____

- - - - - - - - - - - - - - - - - -

_____

- - - - - - - - - - - - - - - - - -

_____

- - - - - - - - - - - - - - - - - -

_____

4. egg   doll   Nat   boss   brick

5. Beth   flag   mat   dog   shell

6. cat   stiff   yell   plum   Bud

Dear Family Member,

Have your child cut out the word cards. Tell your child that all of these words are nouns. Nouns are words that name people or things. Ask your child to sort the nouns: one column for nouns that name a person and one column for nouns that name a thing. Extension: Have your child make a sentence with each noun.

egg	chick	man
kid	Jeff	clock
rock	drum	king

Which is the Best?

1. <u>Who</u> had t<u>o</u> huff and puff t<u>o</u> get t<u>o</u> the top?

_____

- - - - - - - - - - - - - - - - - -

_____

- - - - - - - - - - - - - - - - - -

_____

- - - - - - - - - - - - - - - - - -

_____

2. <u>Where</u> <u>are</u> Nat and Beth in snap shot <u>one</u>?

_____

- - - - - - - - - - - - - - - - - -

_____

- - - - - - - - - - - - - - - - - -

_____

- - - - - - - - - - - - - - - - - -

_____

3. <u>Why</u> did Mom and Dot lift Nat up?

_____

- - - - - - - - - - - - - - - - -

_____

- - - - - - - - - - - - - - - - -

_____

- - - - - - - - - - - - - - - - -

_____

4. steps   Jack   rocks   Dot   dress

5   kid   moms   glass   Beth   pill

6. huff   sock   said   Nat   bed

Directions:

Ask your child to cut out the two circles. Pin the smaller circle on top of the larger circle using a brass fastener. Ask your child to spin the smaller circle to make words. Have your child read the words. Extension: Ask your child to copy the words onto a sheet of paper. Modification: Arrange the circles yourself and have your child read the words.

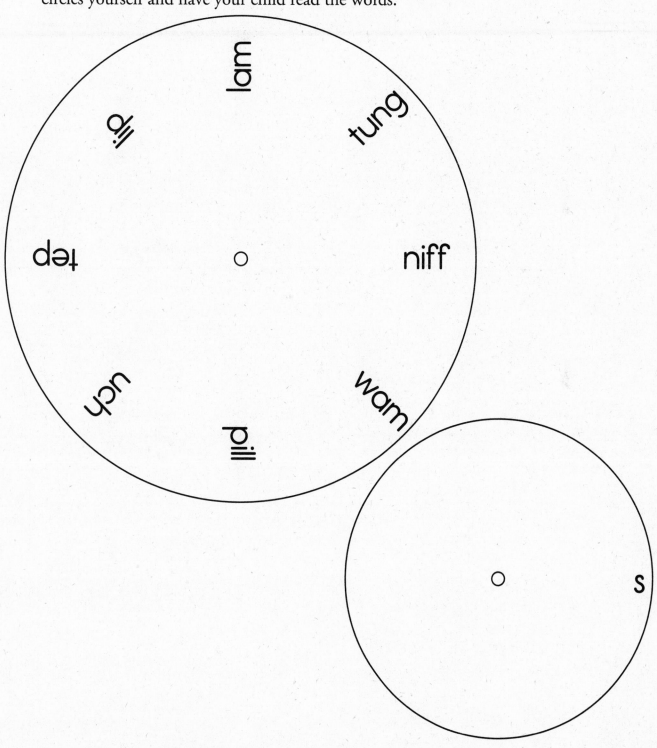

The Bus Stop

It was a big red bus with a top deck.

A thrush was <u>all</u> set to land on Nat's hand.

Nat s<u>ai</u>d that this is the best bus.

Nat, Dot, Beth, and Beth's mom <u>all</u> went to the bus stop.

Directions: Have the student copy or paste the sentences onto Worksheet 29.1 in the correct order.

Directions: Have the student paste the sentences from Worksheet 29.1 onto this worksheet in the correct order. Then have the student illustrate each sentence.

1.

2.

3.

4.

On the Bus

1. <u>Where</u> did Nat and Beth sit on the bus?

_____

- -

_____

- -

_____

- -

_____

- -

_____

2. The bus went past . . .

    ○ a wind mill.

    ○ Big Ben and <u>two</u> sheds.

    ○ a big shop and Big Ben.

3. <u>What</u> is Big Ben?

_____

- - - - - - - - - - - - - - - - - -

_____

_____

- - - - - - - - - - - - - - - - - -

_____

_____

- - - - - - - - - - - - - - - - - -

_____

_____

- - - - - - - - - - - - - - - - - -

_____

4. Big Ben went . . .

○ bam bam.

○ click clack.

○ ding dong.

Dear Family Member,

Ask your child to cut out the word cards. Have your child arrange the cards to make questions. Extension: Ask the child to copy the words onto a sheet of paper. Modification: Arrange the cards yourself and have your child read the questions. Note that the tricky parts in Tricky Words are underlined in gray. Please keep the cards for future practice.

★ Who	★ the	★ was
★ When	man	★ What
★ Why	★ there	is
that	★ here	★ Where
	?	

1. _____
2. _____
3. _____
4. _____
5. _____
6. _____
7. _____
8. _____
9. _____
10. _____

1. _____
2. _____
3. _____
4. _____
5. _____
6. _____
7. _____
8. _____
9. _____
10. _____

The Man in the Black Hat

Directions: Have the student reread the story and answer the questions.

1. <u>What</u> is the job of the man in the black hat?

_____
- - - - - - - - - - - - - - -
_____
- - - - - - - - - - - - - - -
_____
- - - - - - - - - - - - - - -
_____

2. Did Beth get the man t<u>o</u> grin?

_____
- - - - - - - - - - - - - - -
_____
- - - - - - - - - - - - - - -
_____
- - - - - - - - - - - - - - -
_____

3. What did Nat do to get the man to grin?

_____

_ _ _ _ _ _ _ _ _ _ _ _ _ _ _ _ _

_____

_ _ _ _ _ _ _ _ _ _ _ _ _ _ _ _ _

_____

_ _ _ _ _ _ _ _ _ _ _ _ _ _ _ _ _

_____

4. Who did Nat get to grin?

_ _ _ _ _ _ _ _ _ _ _ _ _ _ _ _ _

_____

_ _ _ _ _ _ _ _ _ _ _ _ _ _ _ _ _

_____

_ _ _ _ _ _ _ _ _ _ _ _ _ _ _ _ _

_____

Directions: Have the student copy the word onto the left side of the paper, fold it in half, and then write the word from memory on the right side of the paper.

1.

2.

3.

4.

5.

6.

7.

8.

9.

10.

1.

2.

3.

4.

5.

6.

7.

8.

9.

10.

The Man in the Kilt

Directions: Have the student reread the story and answer the questions.

1. Who was the man that Nat and Beth met?

_____

- -

_____

- -

_____

_____

_____

- -

_____

2. The kilt tells us that the man is . . .

○ a Scot.

○ French.

○ from the U.S.

3. What is a kilt?

_____

- -

_____

- -

_____

_____

_____

- -

_____

4. kilt   dog   clock   Todd   stamp

5. word   Scot   rug   king   man

6. pub   U.S.   twig   Rick   tell

Directions: In line 4, have the students mark the nouns that name a thing; in line 5, have them mark the nouns that name a person; in line 6, circle the nouns that name a place.

Dear Family Member,

This is a story your child has read at school at least once, possibly several times. Encourage your child to read the story to you and talk about it together.

The Bus Stop

Dot led us to a bus stop. At the bus stop th**ere** w**as** a thrush.

Nat held up his hand. The thrush w**as a**ll set t**o** land on his hand, but then Dot s**ai**d, "Nat, stop that!"

Nat let his hand drop.

At the bus stop, Nat s**ai**d, "Beth, this is the best bus!"

I s**ai**d, "**Why**? Is it fast?"

"N**o**," Nat s**ai**d, "it is not that fast."

"Then **why** is it the best?"

Just then, Nat s**ai**d, "Th**ere** it is!"

It w**as** a big red bus with a top deck!

Directions: Have the student trace and copy the letters. The student should say the sounds while writing in the letters.

i   i

i   i

e   e

e   e

a   a

a   a

u   u

u   u

o   o

o   o

i

e

a

u

o

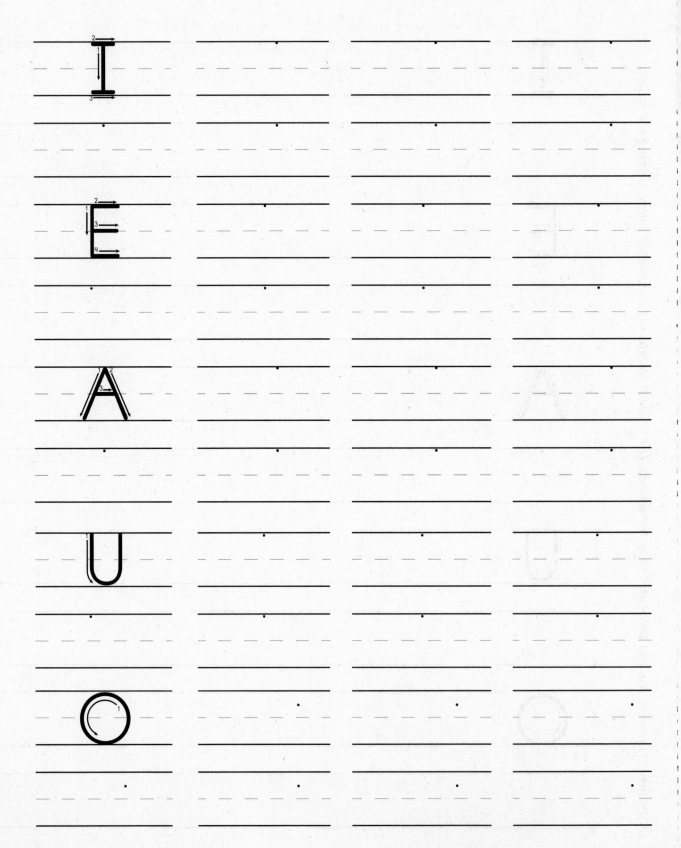

Directions: Have the student trace and copy the letters.

ch

ch

sh

sh

th

th

qu

qu

ng

ng

ch

sh

th

qu

ng

g g

t t

f f

b b

d d

p p

Directions: Have the student trace and copy the double-letter spelling.

g g

t t

f f

b b

d d

p p

Name _____

Directions: Have the student trace and copy the letters. The student should say the sounds while writing teh letters.

m

n

l

r

s

z

m

n

l

r

s

z

Directions: Have the student trace and copy the letters. The student should say the sounds while writing the letters.

M

N

L

R

S

Z

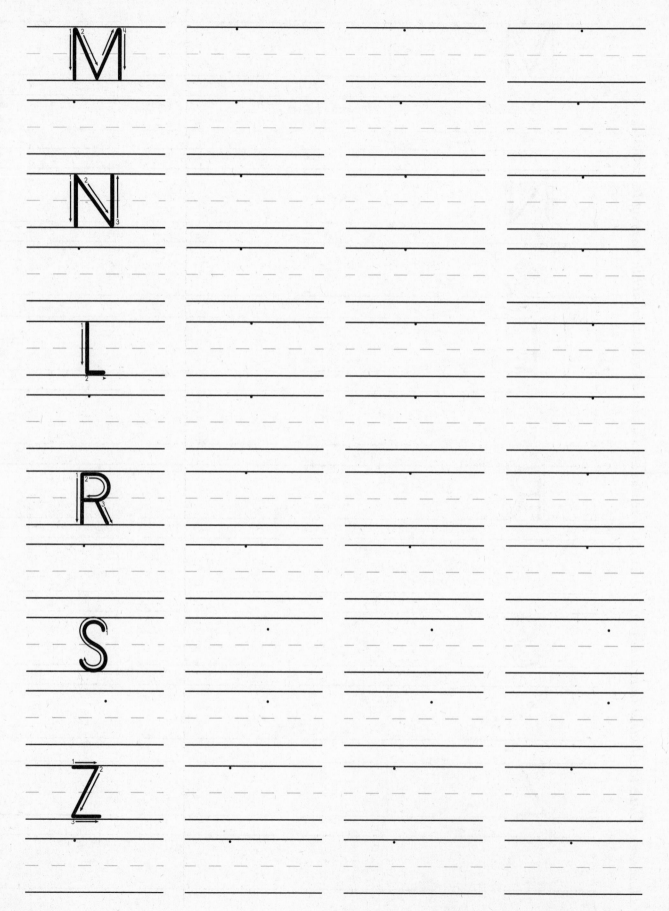

Template for Fishing Pond Exercise

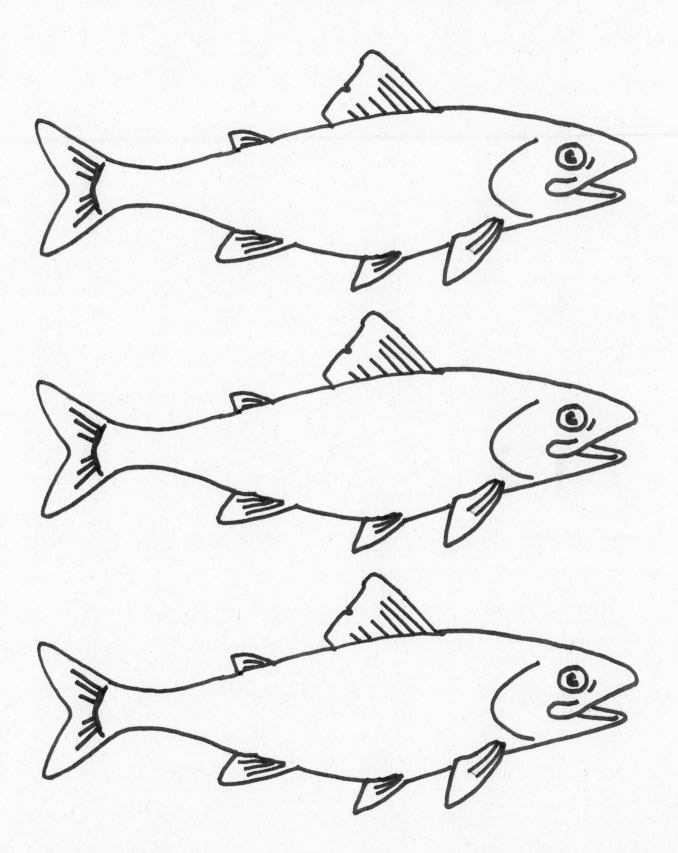

Directions:

  Ask your child to cut out the word cards. Have your child arrange the cards to make phrases. Extension: Ask your child to copy the phrases onto a sheet of paper. Modification: Arrange the cards yourself and have your child read the phrases. Note that the tricky parts in Tricky Words are underlined in gray. Please keep the cards for future practice.

the	a	to
sat	and	has
Greg	in	one
pig	ran	shed

| crack an egg | sit on grass |
| bring <u>a</u> stick | <u>tw</u>o bricks |

_____

_____

Directions: Have the student read the words and phrases. Then have the student write the matching word for each phrase on the line.

dress	tub	soft
pond		ring

_____

1. _____ the bell

2. black _____

3. _____ chick

4. frogs in _____

5. fill the _____

t<u>wo</u>	glass	w<u>o</u>rd
<u>h</u>ere		smell

Directions: Have the student read the words and phrases. Then have the student write the matching words for each phrase on the line.

1. milk in _____

2. _____ quilts

3. bad _____

4. spell the _____

5. sit _____

Directions: Have the student create phrases with the words and write them on a piece of paper.

the	a	two
black	and	one
hat	big	quilt
dress	best	kings

fish	Why	There
Who	kilt	hill

1. Jack and Jill went up the

_____ .

_____

2. _____ is no one here.

_____

3. Nat has a cat and _____ .

4. Beth and Nat met a man in a

_____ .

_____

5. _____ did Dot's map rip?

_____

6. _____ has a pet?

Directions: Have the student read the words and sentences. Then have the student write the matching words for each sentence on the line.

Directions: Have the student read the words and sentences. Then have the student write the matching words for each sentence on the line.

pig	fish	from
licks	sand	cracks

1. The crab runs on the _____.

2. The cat runs _____ the dog.

3. The chick _____ the egg.

4. Do _____ swim in the pond?

5. The _____ digs in the mud.

6. The dog _____ Mom's hand.

?		.
When	Where	do
Who	are	The
here	did	was
kids	that	cat
the	jump	run

Directions: Have the student read the question words and questions. Then have the student write the matching question word for each question on the line.

When	Where	Why
What	Who	Which

1. _____ did the dog rip?

2. _____ is Dot?

3. _____ man had a kilt on?

4. _____ did the man in the black hat stand?

5. _____ was Bud at the vet?

6. _____ was Beth sad?

Directions: Have the student read the Tricky Words and sentences. Then have the student write the matching Tricky Word for each sentence on the line.

Some	Once	All
says	Where	from

1. I got a gift _____ Dad.

2. _____ chicks are soft.

3. _____ there was a strong king.

4. _____ did Tom fling the rock?

5. Josh _____ that one plus one is two.

6. _____ kids have pets.

Dear Family Member,

This is a story your child has read at school. Encourage your child to read the story aloud to you and talk about the events in the story. If your child has difficulty reading a word, encourage your child to blend the word letter by letter to read it.

The Flag Shop

Mom and I went in a lot **of** shops in th**e** U.K. **One of** the shops w**a**s a flag shop.

Th**e** shop had th**e** U.S. flag, the French flag, and th**e** U.K. flag.

That's Mom in th**e** snap shot, with th**e** U.S. flag.

Th**e** U.K. flag has a big red cross on it.

Nat and his mom held **one** up.

I got this snap shot **of** the **tw**o **of** them with th**e** flag.

Dear Family Member,

This is a story your child has read at school. Encourage your child to read the story aloud to you and talk about the events in the story. If your child has difficulty reading a word, encourage your child to blend the word letter by letter to read it.

Which is the Best?

This is a snap shot Mom got.

All of us had t**o** run up a bunch **of** steps t**o** get t**o** this spot.

Nat and I ran up fast. The moms had t**o** huff and puff t**o** get t**o** the top.

This next snap shot is **one** that I got. It is Nat with a bunch **of** big rocks.

Nat had Mom and Dot lift him up.

Then Nat s**ai**d, "Beth, get a snap shot **of** this! I am the rock on top! Get it?"

S**o wh**ich snap shot is the best?

This is a story your child has probably read at least once, possibly several times, at school. Encourage your child to read the story to you and then talk about it together. Note that the tricky parts in Tricky Words are underlined in gray.

The Man in the Kilt

Once Nat and I met a man in a kilt.

I said, "Why is that man in a dress?"

Nat said, "That is not a dress. It is a kilt."

"A quilt?"

I said. "No," Nat said. "A kilt."

"What is a kilt?" I said.

Mom said, "The kilt tells us that the man is a Scot. The cloth on the kilt tells us where the man is from."

"So the kilt tells us his past?" I said.

"Yes," said Mom. "It is a bit of his past."

Mom got this snap shot of us with the man in the kilt!

This is a story your child has probably read at least once, possibly several times, at school. Encourage your child to read the story to you and then talk about it together. Note that the tricky parts in Tricky Words are underlined in gray.

The Map

Once all of us were on a trip when a dog ran up and bit the map.

Dot said, "Bad dog! Stop that! Drop that map! Drop it!"

But the dog did not drop the map. The dog ran up the block with the map.

Nat ran to get the map, but Dot said, "It is just a map. Let the dog have it."

Just then the dog let the map drop. Nat got it and held it up.

"Here it is," Nat said. "But it's got a big rip in it."

"Well," Dot said, "I am just glad the dog bit the map and not one of us."

Name _____

This is a story your child has probably read at least once, possibly several times, at school. Encourage your child to read the story to you and then talk about it together. Note that the tricky parts in Tricky Words are underlined in gray.

Lunch at the King's Pub

At the King's Pub, <u>a</u>ll of us had fish and chips.

<u>A</u>ll of the pubs in the U.K. sell fish and chips. The fish and chips I had in the King's Pub w<u>ere</u> the best I had in the U.K.

Yum, yum!

Nat had a glass of milk with his fish and chips.

Then his hand hit the glass. Splash!

The milk went on Dot's fish and chips.

This snap shot tells it <u>a</u>ll.

Lunch at King's Pub

1. Nat, Dot, Beth, and Beth's mom went to the King's Pub to . . .

    ○ sit with the king.

    ○ get lunch.

    ○ have a chat.

2. Did Beth get to sit with the king?

    _____

    _____

    _____

    _____

    _____

    _____

    _____

Directions: Have the student reread the story and answer the questions.

3. The pub has the best . . .

○ squid and chips.

○ plush beds.

○ fish and chips.

4. squid   map   Dot   brush   pills

5. Nat   fish   Beth   lunch   Dot

6. chips   sit   cab   posh   with

Directions: In line 4, have the students mark the nouns that name a thing; in line 5, have them mark the nouns that name a person; in line 6, have the student mark the nouns.

Lunch at the King's Pub

1. <u>What</u> did Beth, Nat, and the moms get at the pub?

_____

- - - - - - - - - - - - - - - - -

_____

- - - - - - - - - - - - - - - - -

_____

- - - - - - - - - - - - - - - - -

_____

2. <u>What</u> do all the pubs in the U.K. sell?

_____

- - - - - - - - - - - - - - - - -

_____

- - - - - - - - - - - - - - - - -

_____

- - - - - - - - - - - - - - - - -

_____

3. <u>Wha</u>t did Nat hit with the back of his hand?

_____

- -

_____

- -

_____

- -

_____

- -

```
┌─────────────────────────────────┐
│                                 │
│                                 │
│                                 │
│                                 │
│                                 │
│                                 │
│                                 │
│                                 │
└─────────────────────────────────┘
```

_____

- -

_____

Directions: In the box, have the student illustrate a part of the story and then write a caption below.

The Trip Back

1. Was Beth glad <u>wh</u>en the trip had to end?

   _____
   - - - - - - - - - - - - - - - - -
   _____
   - - - - - - - - - - - - - - - - -
   _____
   - - - - - - - - - - - - - - - - -
   _____

2. <u>Who</u> got on the jet?

   _____
   - - - - - - - - - - - - - - - - -
   _____
   - - - - - - - - - - - - - - - - -
   _____
   - - - - - - - - - - - - - - - - -
   _____

Directions: Have the student reread the story and answer the questions.

3. What did Beth get back in the U.S.?

_____

- - - - - - - - - - - - - - - - - -

_____

- - - - - - - - - - - - - - - - - -

_____

- - - - - - - - - - - - - - - - - -

_____

4. What did Beth send Nat?

_____

- - - - - - - - - - - - - - - - - -

_____

- - - - - - - - - - - - - - - - - -

_____

- - - - - - - - - - - - - - - - - -

_____

The Map

```
The dog ran off with the map.
```

```
A dog bit Dot's map.
```

```
Nat said that the map got a big rip.
```

```
Nat ran and got the map back.
```

Directions: Have the student copy or paste the sentences onto Worksheet PP26 in the correct order.

Directions: Have the student paste the sentences onto this worksheet in the correct order. Then have the student illustrate each sentence.

2.

4.

1.

3.

The Punt

Nat and Beth sat still in the punt and did not get wet.

All of them got in the punt.

The man said that the punt can tip.

There were two punts at the dock.

Directions: Have the student paste the sentences onto this worksheet in the correct order. Then have the student illustrate each sentence.

1.

2.

3.

4.

Directions: Have the student reread the stories from the reader Snap Shots and find nouns that name persons or things. Have the student copy the nouns on the worksheet, the nouns that name a person under the picture of the girl and the nouns that name a thing under the picture of the brush.

brush	pal	plum	Kate
clock	nest	Bob	man

Directions: Have the student write the nouns that name a person under the picture of the girl and the nouns that name a thing under the picture of the brush.

_____   _____

_____   _____

_____   _____

_____   _____

_____   _____

_____   _____

_____   _____

Template for Alphabet Wrap

Directions: Have the student connect the letters in alphabetical order with a pencil or string.

a
i
q
c
k
m
g
o
s
e
w
y
u

n
p
d
t
f
l
z
j
v
b
x
r
h

Directions: Have the student connect the letters in alphabetical order. Have the student say the letter names out loud.

e

f   d

j

i

k

h   g   c

l

b

m

n   o

a

z

y

p

t

q

r

v   u

s   w   x

© 2013 Core Knowledge Foundation

Template for Caps Wrap

Directions: Have the student connect the lowercase letters to their uppercase letters in alphabetical order using a pencil or string.

a
i
q
c
k
m
g
o
s
e
w
y
u

Q
M
S
W
U
I
E
K
Y
G
O
A
C

F	L	A	E
I	K	B	G
J	D	H	C

Directions: Have the student copy the uppercase letters next to the matching lowercase letters.

a

e

i

b

f

j

c

g

k

d

h

l

Z	T	Q	U	R
S	V	W	P	Y
N	X	M	O	

m _____ r _____ w _____

n _____ s _____ x _____

o _____ t _____ y _____

p _____ u _____ z _____

q _____ v _____

| ? | . |

Directions: Have the student read the sentences and add a period or question mark at the end of each sentence.

1. Where can I get a snack ☐

2. Dogs and cats are pets ☐

3. I have a big quilt on the bed ☐

4. Who can spell this word ☐

5. The dog can do a lot of tricks ☐

6. When did Jeff get his drum ☐

CORE KNOWLEDGE LANGUAGE ARTS

SERIES EDITOR-IN-CHIEF
E. D. Hirsch, Jr.

PRESIDENT
Linda Bevilacqua

EDITORIAL STAFF
Carolyn Gosse, Senior Editor - Preschool
Khara Turnbull, Materials Development Manager
Michelle L. Warner, Senior Editor - Listening & Learning

Mick Anderson
Robin Blackshire
Maggie Buchanan
Paula Coyner
Sue Fulton
Sara Hunt
Erin Kist
Robin Luecke
Rosie McCormick
Cynthia Peng
Liz Pettit
Ellen Sadler
Deborah Samley
Diane Auger Smith
Sarah Zelinke

DESIGN AND GRAPHICS STAFF
Scott Ritchie, Creative Director

Kim Berrall
Michael Donegan
Liza Greene
Matt Leech
Bridget Moriarty
Lauren Pack

CONSULTING PROJECT MANAGEMENT SERVICES
ScribeConcepts.com

ADDITIONAL CONSULTING SERVICES
Ang Blanchette
Dorrit Green
Carolyn Pinkerton

ACKNOWLEDGMENTS

These materials are the result of the work, advice, and encouragement of numerous individuals over many years. Some of those singled out here already know the depth of our gratitude; others may be surprised to find themselves thanked publicly for help they gave quietly and generously for the sake of the enterprise alone. To helpers named and unnamed we are deeply grateful.

CONTRIBUTORS TO EARLIER VERSIONS OF THESE MATERIALS
Susan B. Albaugh, Kazuko Ashizawa, Nancy Braier, Kathryn M. Cummings, Michelle De Groot, Diana Espinal, Mary E. Forbes, Michael L. Ford, Ted Hirsch, Danielle Knecht, James K. Lee, Diane Henry Leipzig, Martha G. Mack, Liana Mahoney, Isabel McLean, Steve Morrison, Juliane K. Munson, Elizabeth B. Rasmussen, Laura Tortorelli, Rachael L. Shaw, Sivan B. Sherman, Miriam E. Vidaver, Catherine S. Whittington, Jeannette A. Williams

We would like to extend special recognition to Program Directors Matthew Davis and Souzanne Wright who were instrumental to the early development of this program.

SCHOOLS
We are truly grateful to the teachers, students, and administrators of the following schools for their willingness to field test these materials and for their invaluable advice: Capitol View Elementary, Challenge Foundation Academy (IN), Community Academy Public Charter School, Lake Lure Classical Academy, Lepanto Elementary School, New Holland Core Knowledge Academy, Paramount School of Excellence, Pioneer Challenge Foundation Academy, New York City PS 26R (The Carteret School), PS 30X (Wilton School), PS 50X (Clara Barton School), PS 96Q, PS 102X (Joseph O. Loretan), PS 104Q (The Bays Water), PS 214K (Michael Friedsam), PS 223Q (Lyndon B. Johnson School), PS 308K (Clara Cardwell), PS 333Q (Goldie Maple Academy), Sequoyah Elementary School, South Shore Charter Public School, Spartanburg Charter School, Steed Elementary School, Thomas Jefferson Classical Academy, Three Oaks Elementary, West Manor Elementary.

And a special thanks to the CKLA Pilot Coordinators Anita Henderson, Yasmin Lugo-Hernandez, and Susan Smith, whose suggestions and day-to-day support to teachers using these materials in their classrooms was critical.

CREDITS

ILLUSTRATORS AND IMAGE SOURCES

Cover: Shutterstock; Title Page: Shutterstock; Take Home Icon: Core Knowledge Staff; 1.1: Shutterstock; 2.2: Shutterstock; 3.2: Shutterstock; 4.2: Shutterstock; 5.1: Shutterstock; 6.2: Apryl Stott; 6.3: Apryl Stott; 6.4: Kristin Kwan; 6.5: Kristin Kwan; 7.6: Apryl Stott; 7.7: Apryl Stott; 7.9: Kristin Kwan; 7.10: Kristin Kwan; 8.1: Apryl Stott; 8.2: Apryl Stott; 8.4: Kristin Kwan; 8.5: Kristin Kwan; 9.1: Apryl Stott; 9.2: Apryl Stott; 9.4: Kristin Kwan; 9.5: Kristin Kwan; 10.1: Apryl Stott; 10.2: Apryl Stott; 10.3: Kristin Kwan; 10.4: Kristin Kwan; 11.1: Shutterstock; 12.2: Shutterstock; 14.1: Shutterstock; 15.1: Shutterstock; 16.1: Shutterstock; 17.1: Shutterstock; 18.1: Shutterstock; 20.1: Shutterstock; 22.2: Dustin Mackay; 23.2: Dustin Mackay; 32.3: Dustin Mackay; PP7: Core Knowledge Staff; PP9: Shutterstock; PP18: Dustin Mackay; PP19: Dustin Mackay; PP20: Dustin Mackay; PP21: Dustin Mackay; PP22: Dustin Mackay; PP28: Shutterstock; PP29: Shutterstock